The Ballad of the Rocks
and other Writings

Dave Stephen

2QT Limited (Publishing)

This First Edition published 2011 by
2QT Limited (Publishing)
Dalton Lane, Burton In Kendal
Cumbria LA6 1NJ

Cover Design by Robbie Associates
Cover Images supplied by iStockPhoto.com

Printed in Great Britain

Other titles by Dave Stephen:
A Fishy Tail (Hardback with CD)
ISBN 9780956236876
A Fishy Tail (Audiobook)
ISBN 9780956428400

The author has his own website: www.davestephen.com

A CIP catalogue record for this book is available
from the British Library
ISBN 9781908098214

Introduction

When 'A Fishy Tail' was published in 2010, I was asked to look up some other pieces I had written and performed. So here you have a small selection of poems and other writings that I have composed over the years, ranging from the serious to the absurd.

The inspiration for the writings in this volume come from many sources:

Finding a stone from Peterhead on a beach near Caernarfon led to research into Victorian working class life and the creation of 'The Ballad of the Rocks'.

A ticking clock triggered childhood memories of my grandma and aunty in 'Grandma's Room'.

Sometimes it is just the sounds of words and the joy of the variety of words and language, as in 'A Creeping Madness' or 'The Haystack Inspector'.

Most of the pieces in this volume were written for creative workshops and to be performed, so read them aloud if you can.

Hopefully some of them will make you think while others might make you smile.

I hope you enjoy them as much as I have enjoyed creating them.

D.S.

Contents

BUFO - BUFO

In a pool during Spring, as an egg in a string of eggs, I began.
From that egg I emerged, driven on by an urge -
a life force – primeval, much older than man.
As a tadpole, in water I swam with a sort of
wriggling, wiggling, tail-wagging motion.
My back end I would swish, very much like a fish
that lives in the vastness of the deep blue ocean.
And like fish there were shoals of us.
Sometimes crammed into holes, as we hid from the crow,
or the heron that stood like a statue, so totally still,
that you forgot it was there and thought it was safe, 'til:-
a dagger-sharp beak with a murderous technique
was slashing and stabbing and grabbing its dinner.

And then it was calm.
Although I'd suffered no harm,
an observer would see that our numbers were thinner.

It poured with rain, and with nowhere to drain,
the pool level grows and overflows.
And some of our number go with that flow,
following it to where? Who knows?

Then the sun's in the sky and the land starts to dry,
leaving puddles and flooded ruts,
And those of our number in the puddles are trapped,
as the link back to the pool shuts.
For them, there's no way back.
The lucky ones are eaten,
others struggle on in vain.
No more rain comes, the water recedes, desiccates
and for those left, it is too late.

In the main pool we start to metamorphose,
to the point where I even developed a nose
and took air from the surface as my mouth started to grow.
What would happen next was hard to know.
My tail disappeared and I developed some pegs,
which not long after that turned out to be legs.
My head's realigning, then elbows appear.
These things that I'm growing are arms, it seems clear.
And I can crawl and I can breathe
and I can burrow and I can leave
this place.
I'm totally changed,
I'm re-arranged,
I'm like a rocket blasting out into endless space.

An amphibian is what I am!

I'm not a frog in a bog,
But a toad,
whose abode, is gardens,
and woodland, fields and, hedgerows.

I don't jump.
I don't hop.
I'm more inclined just to stop
under a rock,
or in a hole where I doze.

And sometimes I sleep, in a warm compost heap,
keeping an eye on the insects that creep, or a slug.
When a fly, happens by, I say:
"Nice to meet you, now I'll eat you, hello and goodbye."
And then out of my mouth shoots my long sticky tongue
And I think to myself, "The Dinner Gong's rung."
And I blink my eyes.
It's not a twitch of surprise.
It just helps me to swallow the slugs and flies.

On my back, it's true, there are poison glands.
But they won't harm you - not human hands.
But they taste pretty foul to a fox or an owl.
Although, hedgehogs and snakes?
Well, what can you make of such disgusting behaviour?
How can you respect a creature that doesn't mind the flavour
of what it chooses to eat?

When it comes to November, there's no need to remember.
I find a nice spot to hibernate.
I sleep when it's cold and I wake when I'm told that it's warmer.
My body says, "It's time to mate."
And so I travel through soil and gravel
and rock and sand and water,
mud and tarmac to the pool where I was born,
where I started as spawn.
For this is my journey back.
I'm driven by an inner force,
through grass and bracken,
sedge and gorse.
I make my way to the breeding pool,
which is where I was born,
of course.

I've a cousin called Natterjack who,
down the middle of the back
has a stripe of bright yellow.
He's an elegant and energetic fellow.
But me?
I'm just the Common Toad: Bufo bufo.
And I can live to be fifty years old.
We were here before the dinosaurs.
Still here when they gave their dying roars.

But as I make my journey back,
as I cross the black tarmac,
there's a new threat,
a new attack.
We Common Toads,
following instinctive codes,
are being slaughtered, on the roads.

CREEPING MADNESS

Jones the Council stood up
straight
and addressed the
assembled crowd.
He said, "I'm taking this
opportunity
to express my thoughts out
loud.
You see, it's come to my
attention,
(in fact, you could say I'm
perturbed).
I have a quandary. It's
peculiar;
I'm a little bit disturbed.
It seems a little strange.
I know, 'There's nowt so
queer as folk',
as they say in deepest
Yorkshire,
but it's got beyond a joke.
It seems to me a creeping
madness,
is enveloping the land.
It's been going on for some
time now:
I'm just trying to understand.

First there was the strange case
of Gareth Plumber (my good friend)
whose attempts at unblocking blockages,
have sent him round the bend.
And only the other morning,
as I was walking down through town,
there was a right commotion happening,
something big was going down.
"Wheeled conveyances for shopping,
they always were a folly!"
screamed the supermarket manager,
as he went quite off his trolley.

And Glyn down in the chemist shop,
pills enough to treat an army,
screamed, "Unguents, creams and ointments,
It's enough to turn you barmy!"
As he pulverised the counter,
and threw a brick at the plate-glass door,
shouting, "There you are and, just like me,
you'll be cracked for ever more."

At the zoo, there's Tom the Keeper,
who looks after the herbivores.
But he's gone completely nuts,
even bananas. And what's more,
there's Giles Apprentice,
who tries to hang a broken door.
Four times it hasn't worked now,
and he's unhinged upon the floor.
Which is hardly surprising really,
his gaffer, Ron (I heard today)
after many years of fixing shelves,
now has a screw loose, so they say.

Then there's old Dai Wicket.
Studied ten years for his umpire's ticket.
After several shots, had his bails knocked off.
He's batty, but then that's cricket.

Nerys Pritchard changed her job,
went from one of shelves- a- stacking
to biscuit making. Now she's crackers
(at least I think she's cracking).
Rhiannon at the emporium
for those who take food serious,
ordered ten thousand different types of cheese,
I think she's gone deli-rious.
Sian Shop and Robin Taxi
listened to 'Blanket on the Ground.'
They fell in love to Tammy Winette,
now they're bonkers (it's got around).

Glenys the geologist,
studying landforms in her attic,
was obsessed with glacial boulders,
now she's going quite erratic.
Gwilym Slabs, the landscape gardener,
all geometrics and precision,
was asked to design a prestige work:
crazy-paving's his decision!
And Ann Jones set up the sanctuary
for accident-prone birds.
But now she's gone plumb cuckoo.
It's getting quite absurd!

The vicar to the parish,
the Right Reverend Eucharist Knock,
had a new bell fitted in the steeple,
to encourage his Sunday flock.
But now he's to be found, upside down,
hanging from the rope.
Bats in the belfry.
Seeing stars.
Apparently there's no hope.
While Eleri the organist, at the funeral of Dick Boon
broke into 'Happy Days are here again'
and she played that out of tune!
I think you'll find (not to be unkind)
that she's been found of unsound mind.

Then there's Rhys from Pont y Bleddyn,
a climber to the core.
Was it the ropes that sent him loopy?
Made him twisted? And what's more,
what about 'The Mighty Mercuro',
trapeze artiste extraordinaire,
who spent his working life gracefully
flying through the air.
Then just last week under the Big Top,
calamity arose.
He became mentally unbalanced
and landed on his nose.
Then there's Morgan mathematician,
doing calculations to work out
the veracity of a benevolent God.
Very odd!

But there is **no** doubt
that Bill the gravedigger, digging holes,
(deep holes for them that's died)
has definitely lost the plot
and now he's certified.
Another one who lost the plot
was Myfanwy, the crime writer.
Now she's writhing in a jacket
as the straps are pulled up tighter.
She became obsessed with poor Tom Butler,
used to follow him about.
"It was him what done it, he's the guilty one,
it's him!," she used to shout.

Mair the village Barber,
trimming hair. A vital social role.
Was it the torture of a thousand cuts
that has driven her up the pole?
And "You there, put a helmet on.
It's a health and safety matter,"
bawls Gwyn the site foreman.
But they say he's as mad as an hatter.
Rhodri, at the College
had started working as a mentor.
But now he's gone demented.
He thinks he is a centaur,
with bow and arrow, two new legs
and the body of a horse.
They tried to take him back home,
but he galloped off of course.

Up at Plas Du Country Park,
Dewi Humphries (the Park Ranger)
started chopping down the trees.
Deranged, the man's a danger!
Angharad Bach, all motorbikes,
heavy metal and Joe Cocker.
Too much head-banging (so it's said)
has driven her off her rocker.

Peter Pugh (racehorse trainer),
his winning trophies on the table,
sacked his jockey, shed his owners.
He's gone very much unstable.
Now Catrin on a trip to France,
left from Cardiff on a plane,
then jumped off a bridge in Paris.
She just went totally insane.

Angela Astronomer
has been staring at the moon
through her telescope for so much time,
they're calling her a loon.
Ffion, working with her wheel
and kiln and glaze and clay,
making rounded receptacles.
Pretty potty I would say!
And finally, at the old folks knees-up
(an event not to be missed).
They formed a circle and danced to Chubby Checker.
They must be round the twist!

And so I ask you carefully to consider what I've said.
What do you all think?
Came the reply,
"Jones. **You're** totally off your head!"

THE OTHER QUEST -
PART THE FIRST

*K*ing Arthur's tales
are often told
of chivalrous deeds
and knights of old,
of Avalon and Camelot
and the jaunt to
find some holy pot.
But one story that
is lesser known,
(never spread, for lack
of telephones in
days of yore).
"Your what?"
you'll say, but I'll reply
"Stop interrupting,
listen, pray".

Now it is said this other quest,
was the planet, for to search.
From north to south, from east to west,
to the very corners of the earth.
"**YOU** must travel far and wide",
said the King with booming voice.
"Who, us?" the nonplussed knights replied.
"Yes, you. You have no choice.
Useless rabble that you be,
if you wish to sit and sup with me
in my pad, at my Round Table,

to be the stars of future fable,
Then you must shout "Hurrah, Hurree.
Yes Sire, it is our destiny,
our bid for notoriety."
But if you think to disagree,
to chew the fat and lean on me,
then, I will see you rot in hell!
Or, at least somewhere ..um...near Motherwell"

Well, the Knights then huddled in a ring
to discuss the proposal from the King.

And after a modicum of mumbling,
a glut of gripes and grumbling,
some grousing here, much tutting there,
discussions, sub-groups everywhere,
Sir Lancelot spake, his voice did ring
through the gathering gloom,
"Now here's a thing,
as the shop steward for the assembled Knights
as the protector of their employment rights,
as elected rep of those what fights for you,
(and sees some terrible sights).
As soon as we can sort out:
the Health and safety rules,
provision of the correct working tools
and bonus payments, unsocial hours,
protective clothing, statutory powers,
sickness pay and time in lieu.
Then!
We will gladly pursue this quest with you!"

"I'll give you free beer" interjected the King.
"OK, that'll do. Forget the other things!"

And with this the Knights, as one, cheered:
"Hurrah, Hurree. Yes Sire. It is our destiny!"

And King Arthur smiled a self- satisfied smile,
and twisted his moustache.
He thought, "'Tis time to look most regal,
show style and some panache."
And he affected a King-like pose
(which meant that the Knights could see right up his nose).

He thought: I must be careful not to gloat,
"Ahem" he said. He cleared his throat.
"So, pay attention my loyal crew
and I will carefully tell to you
the mission on which we must embark,
when the light of dawn overwhelms the dark
and the mists over Avalon dissipate."
(He liked that word, it sounded great!)

"YOU must travel far and wide
and bring back here from every side,
the most wondrous creatures that there be,
from on the land, from in the sea.
From desert sands to steamy creeks.
From the cold waste lands to mountain peaks.
From rivers, lakes, swamps and bogs.
From in tree tops, from under logs.

Because I announce, by Royal Decree:
The Quest for a Menagerie.
And, gathered comrades, pals and friends,
when our quest eventually ends
and our specimens are collected here,
to marvel at, or perchance to fear.

Then people will sing your praises.
'What great blokes', they'll shout, or similar phrases.
And you can all be pretty chuffed,
gob-smacked, well-pleased, totally stuffed.

And folks will come from near and far,
eventually by motor car
and we will charge them parking fees
and sell them buttered scones and teas,
and celery sticks with cottage cheese.
We'll have numerous opportunities
to make a load of dosh."

"Gosh!" said the bold Sir Tegyr.
"What a massive bad idea.
Bad as in good, Man, know what I mean?
Am I making myself quite clear?"

"But please Sire", said Sir Morded
as he raised a questioning hand,
"I'm afraid I'm not very well-read
and there's somefink I don't understand.
That stuff what you said earlier, Sire.
What is a motor car?"
"Well, to be absolutely straight with you,
I'm not sure what they are."

But Merlin wizard, great magician,
Court soothsayer had a vision.
A future seen, forsooth he saw
and what he saw he said, what's-more!
"Of motorways. Of patios,
and some devise to trim a hairy nose
And a machine where you're in constant touch

although never really say that much.
Of people paid a King's ransom,
to prance about looking handsome.
Or play on a field as a 'football star',
booting a pig's bladder under a bar,
or between some sticks.
And there are things called free kicks.
It all sounded pretty cool,
although I couldn't understand the 'off-side rule'."

"Methinks Merlin's been supping the strong stout beer, "
whispered Bruno le Noir to Sir Alylmere.
"More likely the concoction sold by Bandy Legs Hugh
for three ha'p'ence one farthing, for a quart or two,"
said Dagonet.

"Quiet in the ranks and I will continue,
or at least I'll attempt to explain to you,
that folks will come from near and far,
eventually by motor car (whatever that is).
And the punters will gaze in disbelief,
and gasp: 'Gadzooks, forsooth, good grief!
What kind of creature there is that,'
And 'Well dear, oh dear, I'll eat my hat!'"

And so the brave and noble band looked up at Arthur,
who, with sword in hand
and adopting his most powerful pose,
spoke to the assembled rows:
"We hereby enter a solemn undertaking,
a pact no mortal can consider breaking.

And to send you forth
I will give you my motivational address;
Care of: Dolly Roberts
East of Chipping Sodbury.
Ha, ha, just a jest!
Although I find it quite uplifting!"

And with this the Knights, as one, cheered:
"Hurrah, Hurree. Yes Sire. It is our destiny!"

And so they supped their ale
and swords were sharpened,
a great wassail until the evening darkened
and tales were told of the exploits bold,
and of things to come; what might unfold.
And a warm glow enveloped the assembled throng
as they all joined in singing a tuneless song,
the gist of which was the coming quest.
We leave them as the sun sets in the west.

GRANDMA'S ROOM

I smell coal dust, soot and lavender
a whiff of polish, damp, faint mould
and the tick tock of the mantle clock
and suddenly I am 5 years old
and in my grandma's living room.
There are odours of linoleum and rugs
and the huff huff of the Jeyes Powder puff,
to kill the wood lice and the bugs.

A whiff of old newspapers.
It's something we were used to.
And the rip rip, as they're torn into strip
for the hook in the outside loo.

And the aroma from that holy place?
Well, I'll just call it, a bit of a pong.
And the hum hum, which I'm sure you can hear,
is that someone rehearsing a song?

A bouquet of violets and roses
And the acetone of lacquer from her hair.
And the 'Come here, come here,' that she's calling
while I'm hiding on the stair.

"Have I got his scent, where is he?
I'll give him a big sloppy kiss for a treat."
I feel the boom boom of my pounding heart,
which I'm sure will miss a beat.

Aunty Pearl is making great sport
and she plays the game with glee.
And swish swish go the curtains and doors,
as she sniffs out her prey: that's me!

And then finally she discovers me
in my hiding place behind the drape,
and 'gotcha, gotcha', as her arms entwine.
Smothered in her fragrance, there's no escape.

And she kisses me and chortles.
Pressed to her bosom, I taste lipstick
and 'yuck yuck' as I squirm and buck,
I'm nearly crying. Feeling sick.

And then out of the house I'm running,
past the dustbin's rotting reek,
with the 'slap slap' on the cobbles
of my shoes, as I solace seek

under the railway viaduct,
at the end of the cul de sac,
with the 'chank chank' of the goods wagons
as they're shunted into lines on the track.

Carbolic soap and boiled cabbage.
The rattle of the pot on the brew.
And the 'Click clack' of the needles
as grandma knits a scarf or two.

RON EGYPTIAN

They called him Ron Egyptian,
and I used to wonder why.
But I wouldn't ask him to his face,
as you know I'm a little shy.

Plus the fact that he was bigger than me
and was handy with his fists
and came with a reputation:
"Watch him, he gets red mists."

So I asked about, but surreptitiously-
furtive, like a thief.
Hugger-mugger. Cloak and dagger.
For it was my belief
that Ron wasn't very happy
with the nickname that he had.
No one used it to his face,
I assumed it made him mad.

I asked, "Has Ron ever been to the pyramids,
to the sphinx or down the Nile?
Or has he relatives from the far off Pharaoh land? "
I'd question with a smile
and a finger up against my lips,
(a conspiratorial gesture).
Is his dad from round here? Answer came
"No, I think he came from Leicester"
Well, what about his mam or gran:
"No, they've been here for generations"
Well has he any family links to other far off nations?

And the answers came back no
and no and no and no again,
And I was starting to think
that I would never know the reason - when:

One day I met a bloke who said
he'd been with Ron at school
and out of pure frustration,
I broke my golden rule, because
stealth had got me nowhere.
So I just blurted it right out
"They call him Ron Egyptian –
well, what's that all about?"

And he smirked and grinned and slapped a thigh.
He laughed and slapped some more.
I asked him for a second time,
but he just laughed the more.
"Well, you see we went to a rough old school,"
he said with moistened eyes.
And then he laughed and coughed and wheezed,
I thought that he might die.

By now this was annoying me so I said:
"Well, what's so funny?"
He said "You see Ron was
the only one in school
who called his mother
'MUMMY.'"

BARROWS AND HARROWS

For barrows and harrows. For lawn rakes and stakes.
For pot plants and plant pots. For whatever it takes.
For strimmers, hedge trimmers, plant food and slug pellets.
Lawn mowers, seed sowers, garden growers - we sell it!

Steel shovels and forks, woodsheds and bean stalks
Best topsoil, canned chain oil, pond liners and all.
For string, canes and twine, chain fencing, house signs.
Fence posts, iron railings, and heathers and pines.

We stock barbed wire and barbecues. Buckets, bamboo,
garden gnomes for your homes and there's slate paving too,
sharp sand, stone and slabs, sickles, scythes, secateurs,
spray, powders and potions for when pest plagues occur.

So come browse our merchandise, see what we sell
And soon you'll agree what we all know so well.
A good buy from Goadby, a goodbye from our staff.
Our prices won't lead you up the garden path.

BALLAD OF THE ROCKS

Duncan Brown, a labourer of Kirkton of Skene,
did, on the 3rd day of January 1882 cause an affray, seen
being drunk and disorderly in the town of Aberdeen.
Worse still his violence was directed at a neighbour.
And for this felony, he was sentenced to twelve months hard labour.

So, as a convict, he was transported to the gaol in Peterhead.
Approaching that stark, bleak edifice,
Duncan Brown was filled with dread.
For, Peterhead Gaol was built on the rocky Salthouse headland
which juts out into the cold North Sea. Three storeys to withstand
the raging winter storms, freezing fogs and the stinging spray,
plus the icy blasts from Siberia that tried to blow a man away.
Many who were sent there, never recovered from the ordeal.
They were broken, sick, tormented, or lashed to
crime's ever turning wheel.

Now granite is a hard, hard rock. It's crystalline and rough,
It's made from mica, quartz and feldspar plus some other bits of stuff.
At the local granite quarry, Duncan Brown was put to work,
one cold gloomy morning, in a soaking North Sea murk.
To break the granite into stones the size of a man's fist,
and for one year, the granite was the only reason he'd exist.

Dafydd Amlwch turned his collar up, against the wind and rain.
He'd walked halfway up the mountain, to start his work again.
He split the smooth, sharp slates, in the 'gwalia', (an open sided shed).
Six days a week he laboured there, to earn his daily bread.
Although the weather battered him, sometimes froze him to the core,
he considered his a privileged job; he could be operating a saw up in the
sheds, in a deafening din as the blades ground through the rock,

26

and coughing from the suspended dust, caused by cutting
the rock into block.
Or working at the quarry face, hanging forty feet above the ground,
hemp rope wrapped around his body, an iron bar prising
cracks he'd found.

As he prepares to leave the hut, the final slate he cleaves.
It has some interesting features, a kind of pattern, almost leaves.
He didn't normally take much notice; slates looked
more or less the same.
But on a whim he took this piece and on the back
he scratched his name.

The sailing vessel 'Ynys', was built at Nefyn, on the Llŷn;
plied its trade from America to Hamburg and the places in-between.
It carried anything and everything, wood, guano, sugar, lead.
On this trip it carried roofing slates from Caernarfon to Peterhead.
On board were the captain, Joseph Jenkins, and his crew,
although crew is such a grand word, it was a lad called Dylan Pugh.
Sixteen years old, a bit hot-headed, he'd been at sea for two.
Dylan had a troubled past, he'd never known his mum or dad.
When he left the orphanage, what he wore, was all he had.
When he was in his darker moods, he would brood and quietly fume.
It was said that Dylan Pugh could pick a fight in an empty room.
On that day he left the orphanage he was asked
"What are you going to do?"
And looking out beyond the walls, he said: "What I know is true,
is I'll make my fortune and live in style."
This was met with much derision.
"My prediction for you, young man, is the gallows, or the prison."
And with these words ringing in his ears,
from that place he was despatched.
"Well, if nothing else" he told them, "I know I'm never coming back."

In Peterhead, the 'hard labour' gang was toiling in the quarry.
A ten hour shift, the hammers rang, you didn't stop or you'd be sorry.
The cart with broken granite on was leaving for the dock, and
as it passed by Duncan Brown, it collected one more piece of rock.
A jagged piece of red granite, a little redder than the rest.
He placed it carefully on the cart and then he crossed his chest.
Although these were 'hardened criminals', the warders could be lax,
and many things would carry on when the 'screws'
had turned their backs.

Now, Alex Macalister was a brute, a cruel and vicious man.
After crimes of violence, his reward? Peterhead: a five year span.
He preyed on the other convicts, made their misery much greater.
He stole from them, he bullied them, he played 'the great dictator'.

They found Macalister lying down, which was a punishable offence.
But he would get no punishment, at least not in this world hence.
It was plain to see to everyone, Macalister was dead.
And the only visible evidence was the gash upon his head.
But accidents do happen in quarries and like places
and all the warders' questions were met with dead-pan faces.
No one had seen anything. No, nobody had a clue.
But the warders preferred a quiet life, not fuss and hullabaloo.
Perhaps he'd had a heart attack, cut his head as he took a fall.
Was it worth investigating? He was a convict after all.
So Macalister was covered up, as were the details of his demise,
and no-one seemed to care about that, or react with much surprise.

There were two possible routes by sea from Caernarfon to Peterhead.
One went up around the top of Scotland, the other cut through instead.
The first route was the coastal one, of just over 500 miles;
The North Channel, past the Isle of Man, then via the Scottish isles,
Up around Cape Wrath and then through the Pentland Firth.

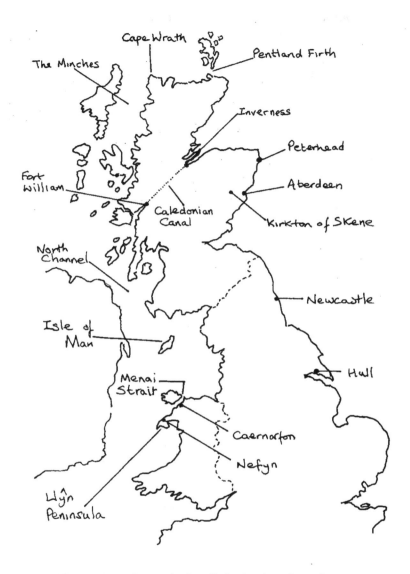

The other, through the Caledonian Canal, was
"more trouble than it's worth,"
said Captain Jenkins, "queuing for the locks, 29 of them all told.
By the time you get to Inverness you've worked your time fourfold.
We'll stick to the open sea, lad, plain sailing, far less work.
Although, when I say less work, that don't mean **you** can shirk."
And Dylan cooked, climbed the rigging, trimmed the sails,

swabbed the decks,
coiled the ropes, pumped the bilges, carried out
the maintenance checks.
And sometimes he took the helm, so the Captain could have a break,
a bit of shuteye in his bunk. And in those moments did awake
inside him a sense of what could be, a type of yearning, a sort of ache.
"I'll make my fortune, live in style" his words came back again
and for those few hours in sole command, Dylan was king of his domain.

Dafydd Amlwch had never doubted that he would work up on the hill.
After thirty years of toiling, his father worked there still.
In the distance was the open sea, sparkling in weak sunlight.
Triangles and rectangles of ships' sails picked out in white.
Dafydd shivered slightly as he surveyed that vast expanse.
Why not emigrate, start a new life? Could he take the chance?
Or was he bound to this place, somehow tied to his ancestry
A prisoner to circumstance, was this his destiny?
Dafydd now was seventeen, fit and healthy, in his prime
He knew that if he was to leave, now was the right time.

Up in Peterhead Quarry, Duncan Brown was breaking rock.
As he looked out to the sea, he saw the 'Ynys' in the dock.
11 months he'd been in this accurséd place,
smashing granite every day.
Apart, of course from Sundays, because on Sundays you had to pray.
The hammer rose, the hammer fell, the granite fractured, splinters flew
and in the harbour, unloading slates was the sailor, Dylan Pugh.

The Ynys was to sail back to Caernarfon, with mixed freight
of sacks of cloth and feather down (bulky items, but not much weight).
And when the boat was light, it could heel or perhaps capsize.
With the forecast for strong winds, to travel light would be unwise.
"When you've finished off the slate, we need ballast in the hold.
There's granite coming on a cart, broken by convicts, so I'm told,

The work's the same for all of them, every day they're taken out,
To sweat up in that quarry," Captain Jenkins pointed out.
And he and Dylan looking up saw a figure on the horizon,
and Dylan shivered as he saw the biggest man that he'd set eyes on.
But worse than that, he was sure the eyes burned straight into his soul.
A cold draught ran up his spine. Fancy working in that Hole!

Duncan Brown could swear that he had looked into Dylan's eyes.
But it wasn't possible. Too far away. Then he heard the warder's cries,
"Hey you, what d'you think you're doing, writing poetry or dreaming
of escaping? Get back to work, to some hard graft. That'll stop you
scheming."

Down by the North Sea quayside, Dylan Pugh mopped his brow.
He'd finished shifting slates and was taking five, sat on the prow.
The horse and cart arrived. "No rest for the wicked," Dylan sighed.
He had to load the ballast, then the cargo; they had to catch the tide.
The carter was a pleasant bloke, helped load the granite in the boat,
then he stowed the cargo, roped and sheeted, the ship now well-afloat.
Dylan thanked the friendly man, who turned round his horse and cart.
Captain Jenkins re-appeared and they made ready to depart.

Duncan Brown looked out to sea as the laden Ynys sailed.
He watched it catch the wind, held his breath and then exhaled,
and then to his amazement, the sailor raised his arm and waved.
He signalled back, the boat to him was the freedom that he craved.

The trip back home had been hard work. Fighting against the weather.
But as they battled the elements, they lived and fought together.
Captain Jenkins was relentless; he forced the vessel through the foam.
Time was money - money: food, and they were pushing to get home.
When they made the Menai Strait, they caught the tides just right
and they tied up in Caernarfon, in the quickly fading light.

Caernarfon Town was somewhere that Dafydd Amlwch rarely went.
He scarcely had any money left once he'd paid for food and rent.
But he fancied something different, a little treat, and a bit of fun.
So he scrubbed himself, combed his hair, and put his best clothes on.

With the Ynys back in port, a rumour was about.
Dylan Pugh was to take on Emyr John in a bare knuckle bout.
Emyr was acknowledged to be the champion of the town
and Dylan Pugh had boasted once, that he could "beat that clown".
So on a piece of waste ground, the contest was arranged.
A crowd had gathered, wagers made and money was exchanged.
A rough circle scraped into the dirt, became the boxing ring,
And a referee was appointed who stated: "Sportsmanship's the thing.
We want a fair fight. No gouging, scratching.
Remember, this is not a brawl.
It's a knockout, count out, or surrender. The winner takes all."
So, stripped to the waist, and toe to toe, the two men traded blows,
and both of them were floored and hurt (or so the record shows).
After fifteen rounds of battering, Emyr caught a fearful clout
and this time when he hit the deck, he was counted out.
Bloodied and defeated, Emyr John was led away.
He cursed and screamed and hollered "Pugh, you'll regret today."
But Dylan wasn't worried; he was surrounded by the throng
who raised him on their shoulders and carried him along
on a tour of local hostelries where he was plied with ale
And the fight was told and told again, in all its gory detail.

Dafydd Amlwch had never met or even heard of Dylan Pugh
But attracted by the rumpus, he'd joined the crowd to get a view,
and what he saw amazed him, he'd got goose bumps on his skin.
For as he'd looked at Dylan Pugh, it was like looking at his twin.

Dylan Pugh was drunk. Captain Jenkins used to say,
"Alcohol is the Devil's work; you'll not drink while in my pay."

But luckily the skipper had gone visiting, was stopping overnight
For had he seen Dylan in his current state,
he would have sacked him there on sight.

Dafydd Amlwch took a stroll; it was grand down by the sea.
There were boats and sailing ships. He had thoughts of being free
to travel the world, to break out from the daily grind.
To have adventures, see new things. To open up his mind.

No one knows for certain what happened on that night.
It is said that threats were made, and that there was a fight.
But what is known is that two days later, they found
Dafydd Amlwch dead.
His body floating near the dock, with two gashes in his head.
And when they examined these, there were little bits of rock.
They were red grains in the blood stains.

The day after that night, Ynys sailed a little down the Strait,
dumped the ballast overboard and sailed back to port to wait
for the delivery of the cargo, for the next journey out to sea.
They were sailing off to Hamburg. Slate and copper for Germany.

And way up there in Peterhead, Duncan Brown was breaking stone.
Two more weeks and he'd be free, and could at last return back home.
His hands were hardened, calloused, rough,
but he knew he'd done his time.
Many didn't make it through, and he'd been punished for his crime.

In Caernarfon, Dylan Pugh was loading up the slates.
The work was hard, repetitive, his back and shoulders ached.
And as he picked the last ones up, one slate became detached.
And on the back was the name 'Dafydd Amlwch' scratched.

The waves crashed in the waves rushed out.
The rocks were rolled and thrashed about
and what once was jagged was, over time, made smooth.
And as the years past, the rocks would move.
Along the shore the rocks would travel,
carried with shells, stones, sand and gravel.

And then one day I was out for a stroll
on Dinas beach, watching the breakers roll.
I reached down and picked up this stone.
About it, I can tell you all that's known.
On inspection, it's speckled red.
It's a granite stone from Peterhead.
And could it be the very bit
that maybe twice was used to hit?
And this other piece I found that day,
just a couple of steps away,
it's a piece of slate, and I know you'll laugh.
But could this be Dafydd Amlwch's epitaph?

A CHRISTMAS CHEER
(Adapted)

We wish you a Merry Christmas.
We wish you a Merry Christmas.
We wish you a Merry Christmas and a Happy New Year.
Good tidings we bring to you and your kin.
We wish you a Merry Christmas
and a Happy New Year.

Oh, bring us a figgy pudding.
Oh, bring us a figgy pudding.
Oh, bring us a figgy pudding and a cup of good cheer.
Good tidings we bring to you and your kin.
We hope you have a Merry Christmas
and a Happy New Year.

We won't go until we get some.
We won't go until we get some.
We won't go until we get some, so bring some out here.
Good tidings we bring to you and your kin.
We'd like you to have a Merry Christmas
and a Happy New Year.

Now we've tried to ask you nicely.
We've tried asking politely
And we won't go until we get some, so bring some out here.
Good hidings we can bring to you and your kin;
Which means you won't have a Merry Christmas
or a Happy New Year.

Right!
If you don't, then we'll burn your house down.
If you don't, then we'll burn your house down.
If you don't then we'll burn your house down, then drink
some more beer
Some threatenings we bring to you and your kin.
We're warning you about Christmas
and a Crappy New Year.

Well, John's gone to get the matches.
Well, John's gone to get the matches.
Well, John's gone to get the matches - let's make
ourselves clear
Bad tidings we bring to you and your kin;
Bad tidings for Christmas
and a Crappy New Year.

Well, this is your final warning.
Well, this is your final warning.
Well, this is your final warning; we've made that quite clear.
Last chances we bring to you and your kin;
Last chance for a Christmas
and a Happy New Year.

Well, you can't say we didn't warn you.
Well, you can't say we didn't warn you.
Well, you can't say we didn't warn you - now we'll disappear.
Good riddance we sing to you and your kin;
Good riddance for Christmas
and you won't see the New Year.

THERE WAS A BLOKE

There was a bloke I worked with once, as in, once upon a time.
I don't mean 'on one occasion', but, like, in a nursery rhyme.

But let me press on, and by that I don't mean to apply pressure,
but to make progress with the story about this bloke,
(who came from Cheshire).

The point of this story, and by point I don't mean a sharp
or tapered end,
or a scoring system in a game, or a headland that we defend.
I mean the essential concept of the narrative,
the purpose of this story.
The outstanding or effective idea. The nub.
The kernel, in all its glory.
That's not an officer in the army, all dressed up and on parade.
I mean, as in the inner essential part of a nut; central core.
Point made?

So anyway, this bloke I knew, he got invited to a ball.
That's a formal dance, not the spherical object;
I don't mean that at all.

So there he is, and he decides that he needs buy a suit -
Not as in hearts, diamonds, cards.
Matching clothes and tie to boot.

And when I say 'to boot', I don't mean to kick about, I mean
'in addition to'. You see, without the tie
they'd probably throw him out.

And the tie is a piece of cloth by the way, worn around the neck,
not being on the same score, like some sporting events
you check.

And when I say 'you check', that's not as in trying
to arrest motion,
or drawing squares, but: inspecting performance or condition.
That sort of notion.

So, where was I? Oh and I don't mean in time and space,
because obviously I've been here all the time,
sitting in this place.
I mean in terms of the story, the tale that I was
trying to tell you.
As in 'recount', though not the hyphenated version, it's true,
because that's what they do in elections.
It's not the same at all.

So, about this trip to buy his suit,
but that's not 'trip' as in taking a fall.

Oh this is getting ridiculous;
I think I'm being too meticulous.
It's obviously getting absurd
having to explain every other word.
I don't want to be pedantic,
or do I mean semantic?
But misunderstandings do get in the way.
Oh forget it.
It's a rubbish story anyway!

THE OTHER QUEST - PART THE SECOND

*S*aid King Arthur: "Now, Sir Galahad,
methinks thou art a trifle sad.
You look downcast. What vexes thee?
Perchance you are annoyed with me?
Art thou worried by the coming quest?"

"No Sire, I've packed my thermal vest.
I'm up for it. I'm lean and fit.
I'm guaranteed to do my bit.
I was just pondering where I should roam,
to bring a fitting creature home
and glorify this undertaking -
the menagerie that we are making."

"Well, Galahad, I have no doubt
that you'll do your very best,
as always in these matters.
I wish that I'd been blessed
with a hundred such as thee -
or fifty, nay ten - or even two.
Although if just two, then I suppose
that would just be me and you!"

So, Galahad put his Sunday armour on
and went off for a stroll, saying,
"I need to have a serious think
and identify my goal."
(For Galahad had attended
a staff development day
about managing by objectives -
the Peter Drucker way.)

And so he clanked and rattled,
clunked and rasped and squeaked
with his trusty helmet visor down,
until suddenly - EEK!
There was a mighty clang upon his bonce.
"I'm being attacked. I do declare,
I've ignored the first rule of knightery
that is:-
Rule 1: to be constantly aware:
a coiled spring, primed and ready
to react to dangers as they arise.
Forewarned, precautions taken
to minimise the element of surprise.
Always be upon your guard.
Be chivalrous and polite, but
Be mindful that almost anyone
may want to bash you on the nut.

As a first rule, this is a bit verbose
I'm sure you would agree
But that's nothing to the grandiloquence
of Rule One hundred and three!"

Galahad drew his sword and swung around,
but getting dizzy, fell to the ground.
And waiting for the expected blow,
when nothing happened, looked up slow
and realised
it was a low branch of a spreading tree
that had ambushed him.
"Oh, Silly Me!" he said
and, lifting up his visor,
he looked sheepishly around
to see if anyone had witnessed
the tree branch knock him to the ground.
It could harm his reputation
if this event had been observed.

He'd worked hard to earn respect.
It was something he deserved.

But you could never be too sure.
Was someone hiding behind a tree?
Laughing at his misfortune, or worse still,
plotting with great glee
his demise. Were they smiling,
waiting to tell about this buffoon knight
who walked into a hanging branch
and very nearly died of fright?

That Merlin was the worst of them.
Always had something up his sleeve.
And I don't mean arms and elbows
but tales you could only just believe.

He was plotting, scheming, gossiping;
power-broking, making deals,
trading influence and twisting arms;
wheels within wheels within wheels.

But maybe this was paranoia?
Perhaps he shouldn't think this way -
although Camelot could be a snake-pit,
a new conspiracy each day!

Galahad gathered up his dignity,
and then puffed out his chest -
which is quite a difficult thing to do,
when you wear a chain-mail vest.

Nonchalantly he walked on, whistling,
until at last he reached a stile
and, climbing over, missed his step
and there he stayed awhile;
stuck lying upon his back,
his legs akimbo in the air,

like an upside down wood louse,
(Oh, life was so unfair!).

Until, a passer-by passing by,
helped him to his feet.
"Hast tha fallen over, bashed thy head?
By gum lad, are thee reet?"

And with that, Galahad replied:
"Thank you, thank you my good man,
I think I am. That's worked a treat.
I've come up with a plan.
Lying on your back
gives you an interesting perspective,
especially when there is a matter
on which you wish to be reflective.

The sky is like an open canvas,
waiting for the artist's brush.
So, what have I learnt?
I've learnt I need to oil my armour.
Staying still caused a wonderful hush
which gave me the peace and space
in which to perform my cogitation.
I've made a monumental decision.
Hence, no more procrastination!

And so I must now hasten back
And tell King Arthur of my scheme
It'll add substance to his 'Other Quest',
show it's not a fool's pipe dream.
Not of course that I'm inferring
that the King could be a fool.
He must be intelligent and wise,
after all, he was born to rule."

So he went with a clank and a rattle,
with an occasional rasp and squeak
As he retraced his steps, he thought to himself:
It's a good job I'm not trying to sneak
up on an unsuspecting enemy
in an ambush or a stealthy attack.
They'd hear me coming from miles away.
As a spy I'd soon get the sack!

So, King Arthur called a meeting
to be attended by all at the Court.
The subject to be: 'The Other Quest:
Our very first Progress Report.'
And the only item on the agenda,
except for apologies and any other bits,
was a report to be given by Sir Galahad.

So the invited throng was assembled,
a gathering of the great and the good -
plus the not so great and the pretty awful,
I'd like to make that understood.

And Merlin started off proceedings
with some spells and incantations
and then a rambling sermon of inordinate length
to do with 'Trials and Tribulations'.

Sir Galahad had counted on going first,
but by now he'd counted to 9002.
Then all of a sudden Merlin said,
"So, Sir Galahad, over to you!"

"Sire, I am going to the land of Tutankhamen."
declared Sir Galahad.
"I know it sounds extraordinary,
very dangerous, but it's not too bad."
He wished he hadn't mentioned the dangerous bit,
it made him feel a little bit nervous.

But he put a brave face on it and said,
"Sire, it's an honour to be of service!"

The King looked on with obvious pride
and said "Sir Galahad, well done.
You are a paragon, a role–model,
an exemplar. Knight number one!"

As Galahad blushed and looked quite smug
there was a buzz of consternation.
Whispered Sir Hector to Sir Tristram,
"Methinks Galahad rises above his station."
There were mutterings, mumblings,
complaints and grumblings.
And growing like a creeping disease,
an undercurrent of unease.

People guffawed, people sneered.
Sensing his moment, Merlin stirred,
He cleared his throat and stroked his beard.
"Sire, if I might have a word?"
Then addressing Sir Galahad he said,
"I would just like to check out some things
I've heard on the grape-vine recently,
carried to me on a little bird's wings."

Sir Galahad was filled with foreboding.
Merlin's expression was one of distaste.
After a pregnant pause, Merlin pointed
a bony finger at Galahad's face.

"I've heard you're **tree**-mendously brave.
I hear you've been **branch**ing out!
It must be a re-**leaf** to **root** out a foe
and fetch them a **wood**-cutter's clout.
I must say also I admire your **Style**!
Who knows where the danger lurks?"

There were sniggers all around the room.
There were whisperings, murmurs and smirks.

So, someone had seen his misfortune,
thought Galahad as he stared at the floor.
Then, swallowing hard he looked around
fighting an urge to run for the door.

"But, I think you'll find.
my brave, bold Knight
you'll be wasting your time.
You'll see that I'm right!

For it's only mice and rats
and a mangy fox
that on Tooting Common live.
There are no flocks
of other beasts.
That's all that you'll find there.

I once got a train from Tooting Bec
on my way to Leicester Square.
Underground, the Northern Line,
it's a case of bad engineering design.
The ticket barrier caught my cloak,
ripped it asunder. That's no joke!

But which **route** would you have taken
Sir or shall we **leave** it alone?
I see you've **twigged** what's going on.
Do you think you may be accident-**prone**?"

Merlin looked around the audience
and acknowledged the nodding heads.
And he smiled and played with a finger-nail,
thinking 'Methinks, I'll be number one instead!'

Sir Galahad looked around, perplexed,
"Sire, Merlin tries to make me vexed.
But he's got the wrong end of the stick."
"Interesting word 'stick',
now who's taking the Mick?"
interjected Merlin straightway.
And he waved to his growing fan-base,
who laughed and tittered and pointed
to where Galahad stood, straight-faced.

"Sire, it is not Tooting Common I go to.
I'm afraid Merlin has clearly misheard.
Or maybe he's loosing his marbles.
Most of his utterings seem plainly absurd!

It is to the land of Tutankhamen
(the boy Pharaoh) that I will travel -
the land of the Pharos and Sphinx
and the bad-tempered Dromedary camel.

For Sire, it is rumoured that a strange beast
lives in the River Nile.
Half dragon, half fish and twenty feet long,
it's called the crocodile.
And I intend to capture two
and bring them back alive for you!"

"I suppose next you'll tell me that fish can walk!"
Merlin spluttered. "What rot you talk."

Galahad looked Merlin straight in the eye
but addressed himself to the King.
"Sire, if I may be permitted to respond to that jibe,
these barbs that Merlin doth fling?"
With a glint in his eye,
Arthur surveyed the crowd,
and with the hint of a smile
stated, "Yes, that's allowed."

Sir Galahad spoke:
"Merlin, I'd not be so rash as to mention
anything that I thought not true.
For, Sir, you twist and spin and invent.
You conjure up things out of the blue.

I've no time for your tiresome game-playing.
I've no interest in loose tittle-tattle.
Well, what do they say about empty vessels?
They make most noise. Such is prattle!

And Merlin, if any it's of interest to you,
I'll tell you plainly what I think.
In one sentence you mention rot and fish.
Put those together and you get a stink!"

Merlin, twisted-smile sprayed on,
said quietly, "Sire, methinks 'twas a vicious attack!
I respectfully request the right to reply.
My chance to answer back."

And looking round the quietened room
you could have heard a thin pin drop.
But no-one dropped one (a pin, that is)
And King Arthur shouted, "Stop!
Methinks we've had much entertainment here,
I admire you both for your pluck.
Were that I was surrounded by hundreds like thee.
But unfortunately, no such luck.

So, Merlin, my counsel, my wizard, my advisor.
And Galahad, my champion, my rock.
Let us all work together. For when we work together,
Gentlemen, up goes our stock!

So let us all join in wishing Sir Galahad
the very best for his coming pursuit.
When he returns with his mission fulfilled
he'll be a Knight of even higher repute!"
So Sir Galahad said goodbye.
"I've prepared a little allocution
to honour this momentous event.
A few key note statements and important points,
outlining the process I underwent
in selecting my current objective,
of the challenges and struggles and stress,
of how I discovered my inner self.
Which was a bit of a mess, I confess.

So, gathered friends, I go to my duty
and as a Knight I will give of my best.
Although this time no pillaging and booty,
will be part of this forthcoming quest.
But I go...
for I go...
and when I go...
I go....
Wherever ....
I may go.
Oh damn, I've forgotten the rest!
But anyway, while you're here in Court
remember where us Knights will be.
Out there in the big bad world,
exploring the land and crossing the sea.
And I will be a distance hence
when you see tomorrow dawning."

"We've got free beer here!" cried the victualler.

"Oh, very well. In that case I'll leave in the morning!"

And so they supped their ale
and swords were sharpened,
a great wassail until the evening darkened.
And tales were told of the exploits bold,
and of things to come; what might unfold.
And a warm glow enveloped the assembled throng
as they all joined in singing a tuneless song,
save for Merlin who was deep in thought
And, if perchance, we could have caught
those musings from that active mind -
would those thoughts have been unkind?

THE COLLECTIST

Now, I have a friend called Mister Hall
Who, keeps fossils in bottles and rocks in socks
Hatpins in tins and some old mortise locks
with keys that don't fit. He's got coins and stamps.
There are straws in drawers and two hurricane lamps,
Bus tickets, photographs, postcards from each year
Plus, an old wooden crate that contained ginger beer.

Now I say, " Mister Hall, you're a collectist,
and I accept the definition is something that's missed."

"No, I'm a collector!" he will usually respond.
"And pray", he will say, "What's a collectist anyway?
'Cos it's a word of which you seem very fond
Even though I know that it doesn't exist
I assure you it's missing from the dictionary list."

I reply, "I accept that there is no such word
I know that it's missing, but that omission's absurd."

"Why, what's the difference?" he asks me.
And I will attempt to explain:
"Well Mr. Hall, you're a collectist
like the difference twixt a tram and a train.
It's an altogether different kettle of fish.
Is a knife a fork? Is a sieve a colander?"
Would you call a saucer a dish?

"You see a collector collects things that are classified;
they are quantified, catalogued, made systematic.
Put in a scheme or order and organised.
And that's why the definition's so problematic
When applied to you Mister Hall.

Now, a 'collectist',
Well, my definition of a 'collectist'?
I'll explain it as best as I can.
They just collect a jumble of assorted bits and pieces
Without rhyme or reason or plan,
higgledy-piggledy, flotsam and jetsam.
Unconnected, like a many-fruit jam.

And how do you name such a process?
What do you call such a mixture of things?
You, Humphreston, old chap, are a collectist!
And it's fantastic the pleasure that brings."

WIND

I heard a story of a mistral,
is that a tailwind do you think?
And is a following wind a stalker?
A downdraught a type of drink?
In it's raging, roaring, howling,
scowling tantrum, the hurricane
Snorts and pants, huffs and wheezes,
and hurls down hail and rain.

Did flappers dance to squally jazz
all through Roaring Forties?
Does the sirocco blow Morocco?
Does the Chinook go out on sorties?
And can I wear my sou'wester
when the wind blows to the west?
And when they swap are they then trade winds?
And is the headwind thought the best?

Now, typhoons and tornadoes
want to blow you half insane.
But if a cyclone worries about appearances,
is that a weather vane?
So when the prevailing winds win
and show on the Beaufort scale,
if the gustiness makes you want to swear,
try a blast, it never fails.

THEOLONIUS MONKFISH WINGNUT

Theolonius Monkfish Walnut
invented a 'wonderful thing'.
It was designed for excursions down to the shops
and he dreamt of the wealth his
invention would bring.

So, after gathering all of the whatnots,
the doobreys and thingamabobs
and a muddle of flotsam and jetsam
(plus a collection of door handle knobs)
he fiddled and fettled and hammered,
whittled and chiselled and scraped,
until at long last he'd finished it
and he shouted out,
"Eureka, mates!
I've completed my labours
neighbours.

Whoopee!!!
Frogs are all croakers.
Life's hocus pocus.
I'm riding down town
on my steel diplodocus."

So T.M.Wingnut, or Theo M.W.
(as he sometimes liked to be called)
set off in a great billow of steam and sparks
(which kept those who looked on enthralled).

With a rattling, clattering and frankly ear-shattering
cacophony of squeaks, burps and bangs,
he rounded the bend at the end of the lane
(with a blast of a whistle from an ancient steam train)
and disappeared from the view of the onlooking crowd
(already obscured in a Wingnut-made cloud).

It clanked, scraped and clunked,
with a noise like a thousand road rollers
being dropped by a crane
from a very great height,
down a huge metal drain,
in the middle of the night.

It was difficult finding a parking place
for a contraption of such a large size.
So he stopped in the road and was duly approached
by the proprietor of a stall selling pies.
"Excuse me Sir, but you can't park that here.
I quote Section Fourteen of the local Byelaws.
"No 'steam-driven gadgets.'
It's perfectly clear.

It's highlighted here in a separate sub-clause.
'If the owner, or person, in charge of said object
shall cause nuisance, or create aggravation,
then it only reasonable to tell them to stop
or report them to the nearest Police Station."
So, Wingnut T.M. or T. Monkfish Nut
(as some people unkindly called him)
gathered himself up to his full five feet two,
took a deep breath and stuck out his chin.
"All you say Sir is drivel and piffle and fudge.
What are you trying to communicate? I can't understand
how you say nothing so cleverly.
It's hard to judge if this is a natural ability,
or if you have it all planned.
But anyway, enough of your bluster and tripe,
I've no time to stand here and grumble and gripe!"

And with that being said, he kick-started the 'thing'
with a tremendous explosion that made you ears ring
and blew the wig off the head of the man who sold pies,
who was bald (as you now probably realise).

The wig caught on the wind
and blew over a wall,
where it was chased by a cat
which knocked over the stall.

The pies were scattered
all over the road,
causing the lorry to skid
and shed its load
of over-ripe bananas
and pots of ice cream
and enough jelly and custard
to feed a whole football team.

Well, the pieman slipped
and fell to the ground
and when he got up,
could hear hardly a sound
because in both of his ears
was squashed fruit and ice-cream.

"I can't hear! I can't hear!"
the man started to scream.

But Theolonius Wingnut
could see what was wrong
and he quickly approached
with a thrummaging prong
(which was invention of his
from several years back
that he carried about in a
tatty old sack,
just in case.....)

"What's your name Mister Pieman?" asked Theo
"What did you say?" was the man's reply.
"What's your name Mister Pieman?" shouted Theo again.
"I'm sorry, can't hear! Don't know why!"

"What's your name Mister Pieman?" bellowed Theo
"Nearly heard you that time. Try again."
"What's your name Mister Pieman?" through a megaphone.
"Not so loud, you'll batter my brains!"

"My name?
Well, I was christened Aloysius Aristotle
Beerbelly Wormbucket Broadshanks,
but people call me Geoff most of the time
on account of my mother being Manx."

"Well, as Theolonius Monkfish Wingnut,
I am qualified to say
that you have a problem with your hearing
caused by events that happened today.
You have fruit, jelly and custard
all stuffed in your ears, Mister Geoff.
I'd say this was a fairly simple case.
My diagnosis?
You're a trifle deaf!

That will be ninety nine pounds fifty
assuming that you pay cash.
And now I must desert you.
Oops!
Your expression -
Time to dash!"

And with that, Monkfish Wingnut (T.M.W. for short)
drove back home as it started to rain.
And over a broccoli, rhubarb and baked bean pie
he vowed that he'd never drive downtown again.

"It's my intention to exhibit my invention
in a 'Museum of Fantastic Things'
(all invented by me, of course!)
Like the wonderful cast-concrete wings
which enable pigs to fly from the sty,
so high in the sky, that they fade from the eye.

Also, the huge umbrella which I specifically designed
with kennels and baskets on top.
It is only deployed for as long as it takes
for the cats and dogs raining to stop."

Theolonius Monkfish Wingnut
opened his 'Things' museum
and as he said to anyone passing by
"You can come right inside and see them.
I'm not trying to make a fortune,
I'm only charging a small amount
and as long as you are honest with me,
I can even put that on account.
And when I've counted up all the fees,
plus the number of shakes of the old bee's knees
and I've sold off the design for my chocolate fire-guard
and auctioned off the rest of my sculptures in lard,
I'll be famous. As famous as the Duke of Galoshes,
Napoleon Blownapart or zinc-coated washers.
There'll be a plaque in the town
which will proclaim:

'Give a cheer,
For Theolonius
Monkfish Wingnut
(famous inventor)
lived here.'

59

DOE

Doe, a deer, a female deer.

Dough, some stuff for making bread.

Dough, spondoolies, shekels, cash.

Doh, what Homer Simpson said.

Dough, slang soldier in the States.

DOE, environment debates.

"Do' do that, Black Country Mates.

That will bring us back to Doe.

THE HAYSTACK INSPECTOR

As the haystack inspector for Shropshire
was frequently heard to complain,
the standards of stacking up hay bales
had most certainly fallen again.

"They should stack them two broad and one across,
no gaps more than the width of my thumb because
a haystack is clearly a work of art.
Not something willy-nilly, just chucked off a cart!".

So she phoned up the local newspaper
and arranged for the front-page headline:

**'ATTACK ON SLACK STACKING OF HAY BALES:
pull your socks up farmers- it's time!'**

They waited for a whirlwind reaction.
Would the farming folk respond?
Would they move all the cows from the cowsheds?
Would they get all the ducks off the ponds?
And load up the tractors and harvesters,
Land Rovers, lorries and diggers,
and drive down to the council offices,
shout the slogan,
"Compensation: six figures!?"

But nothing whatsoever happened.
There was hardly a response at all.
In fact, the phones were as cold as a cucumber
(bought in December from a market stall).

And so left with no other alternative
the editor went to the press,
with the only headline possible
to clear up what was a bit of a mess:

**BACKLASH TO THE LACK OF FLAK
OVER ATTACK ON FARMER'S SLACK STACKING:
HAYSTACK INSPECTOR LEAVES HER POST.
RESIGNATION, OR WAS IT A SACKING?**

TIME

time
tick tocks
the clock
the sands
they run away
we chase about

rush and hurry
fret and worry
speeding hither
dashing thither
trying not to waste our time
and then
when we pause
we try to catch our breath
and having caught it
who'd of thought it?
It frightens us quite half to death
for
where do we keep those
stolen minutes
precious seconds
captured moments
that we are now aware of?

how can we contain an ever-changing
fleeting, flitting all-world ranging
ephemeral phenomenon like time?

so quickly stop procrastinating
the only place for incarcerating
this thief before the last bell's chime
we put it in the nick of time

BALCONY SONG

Picture me sitting in my own front-room
with my radio on. It's playing loud.
When I decide to have a drink,
I get up off the sofa,
I look out of the window and
WOW!
Because there's a man on the balcony
of the tower block right across the street
and I don't think he's joking.
No, I don't think he's kidding.
I think he wants to take the weight off his feet.

I say:
"Couldn't you have picked a better day to do it
because it's cold and it's raining outside.
And my favourite track is on the radio playing
But there ain't nowhere to hide."

So it's out of my room,
out of my door,
out of my block,
out of my mind,
there's so much traffic on the street.
Into his block. Up to his flat.
I'm out of breath because the lift's on the blink.

I think,
"Couldn't you have picked a better day to do it
because it's cold and it's raining outside
And my favourite track is on the radio playing
But I ain't got nowhere to hide."

He says, "Hi!
It's great to meet you.
You know sometimes
I get so lonely I could cry.
There's thousands of people
who live their lives on this street
and every single one passes me by.

But hey, it's nice to talk to you.
Maybe we can go out for a beer
and you can introduce me
to all of your friends
and all the people who live around here."

I say, "Yes, you know that's all very well
but there's something you have to realise.
I've only lived here for five years myself
and I only know a couple of guys."

I think,
couldn't you have picked a better day to do it?
because it's cold and it's raining outside.
And my favourite track is on the radio playing
But I ain't got nowhere to hide.

Picture a man, sitting in his own front-room
With his radio on; it's playing loud.
When he decides to have a drink
he gets up off the sofa,
he looks out of the window and
WOW!
Because there's me, on the balcony
of the tower block right across the street.
And I don't think I'm joking.
No I don't think I'm kidding.
I know I'm going to take the weight off my feet.

GROUSING

(This contains the names of 70 bird species)

"I call for Order in this debating house,"
Martin with great passion cried.
"Feast your eyes on this gold crest up on the wall.
You should be puffing your chest out with pride.

On that badge the guillemot stands for rectitude.
It's a black bird that's wearing a suit.
And the merganser represents endurance,
Of that there can be no dispute."

Then up stood a man who looked quite cross.
Bill Dunnock, he said was his name.
Bald as a coot and with one golden eye,
had a nose ring: a man of great fame.

He wore a ruff on his boiler suit and behind one ear
was a feather from the tail of a pheasant.
His gaiters were knotted; they called him 'Redshanks'-
the only nickname he had, that was pleasant.

"They accused me of robbin' when I was a lad.
I'd worked as a dipper, they said.
And " 'oarding like a magpie", but I tell you, by God,
wits I used. If I stole, strike me dead!

In gaiters bright red, started hawking up town.
'I'm honest, transparent', I'd tell 'em.
I started wiv nuffink except an 'and-cart,
selling eider down, black caps and vellum.

I mixed with the chiff chaff (that's rhyming slang),
but they were the salt of the earth.
Shirts made of burlap, wing collars of card,
but Gad Wally, lad, there was mirth."

"Cor! More ranting and raving than rabies.
Stop crowing, you clucking old hen!"
Shouted blue-bloodied Hesketh Rushworth,
"No doubt we'll get war stories again!"

"See how they treat you, these toffs.
I fought in the war, don't you know.
Fighting rebels and spiteful marauders
with more henchmen; all murderous foe.

The land was part ridge and part furrow.
We protected a small arduous hill.
When the enemy fired off a ten pounder shell,
'Duck, ruddy duck!' shouted Bill.

There's me and Pip, heads down and running,
'til we reached the top of a cliff that was sheer.
Water lapped at the foot of the rock.
'Pip, it's curtains for us now I fear.'

And as the machine guns like woodpeckers rattled,
I shout, 'Pip, no time to be yellow.'
Legs like jelly, as I jumped the barbed wire,
'Ere, 'ave a set of these my good fellow.'

I gave him a set of saucepans.
Pip could be a bit of a wag.
Tales of the old times and derring-do
as we filled up our pipes full of shag.

'What are these for?' Pip asked me directly.
'To store me petrol in,' I joked.
But, actually, it's because it's all gone to pot,
led by bustards like him." Finger poked
at Hesketh and all of his cronies,
lined up on the opposite benches.
"I had more respect for the enemy
who shot at me from the trenches!"

At this the chamber erupted with a cacophony
of squawking and whooping and toots.
Trumpeting, whistling and honking -
not to mention the screeching and hoots.
(I said not to mention the screeching and hoots)

The Right Honourable Shrike had arrived on her bike
and tied it up with a falconer's knot,
to a rail by a gnarly old sycamore tree
(creepers covering up half of the spot).

"Now! I've read polls in the papers, and we can't duck this issue"
she announced to the assembled throng.
"I'm not meaning to grouse or make anyone quail,
but if we don't act soon this could be our swan song.

For the time has gone when we would lark about
with lots of sniping, and tit for tat.
We would cock a snook to the people outside.
Filibuster and ramble: we must put a stop to all that."

Peers Dunlin-Sanderling and Peregrine Yaffle
guffawed and made lots of rude signs.
"That's bally gosh awkward," peers mumbled aloud.
"If I can't keep B***** rambling, I may have to resign!"

The Right Honourable Shrike fixed the pair with a stare
and said, "It's behaviour like that that we need to combat.
We must swallow our pride and clean up our act.
For when the public's consulted, you'll find
that the words that they'd use to describe our behaviour:
nut, crackers and cuckoo spring to mind."

The Other Quest:
Part The Fourth

*S*ir Gawain was a little overweight
and often came to Court quite late.
What with this and his quite sullen trait,
he was a lardy, tardy, mardy mate.
So he moped off to Salisbury Plain.
He searched a bit but then it rained.
So to a tavern he did retire
and, feet up, by a roaring fire
he supped some ale and ate some pie.
Then supped some more, and by and by,
he fell asleep.
And as he slumbered, Gawain snored.

And people spread the news abroad
that a chivalrous Knight was in the pub,
full of ale and full of grub.
And he was on a quest to find
a beast of an unusual kind.

When Gawain awoke he became aware
of a bloke who sat in the very next chair.
He had a wooden leg, patch over one eye,
and things that moved in his hair.

"Hello Sire, Nice to make your acquaintance.
I'm Silas Camm. From Devizes I hail.
My mother was Mad Maud from Malmesbury.
I was born under a hedge in a gale.

Now Sire, it has got about
that you're exploring. Searching out
strange creatures what may exist round here.

I'm so impressed I've bought a beer
for you to quaff while I explain
(you're obviously blessed with a very good brain)
that I may have something for thee.
I have a creature very rare, you see."

"Nice to meet you Mister Camm.
Gawain of Gwynedd is who I am
And it's true, I've been searching Salisbury Plain.
So, go on, go on!" said Sir Gawain.

"Well Sire, this creature, has a pair of wings
and talons, and some other things
which are descended from an eagle.
It has the body and tail of the noble beast,
the ferocious lion from the Middle East.
But don't worry, everything's legal,
I've got the paper work."

"Well goodness me," cried Sir Gawain.
"Does this creature have a lion's mane?"

"Er, possibly..." said Silas.

"Then it sounds to me...
surely, ...it couldn't be
possibly...
could it be......"
a gryphon?"

"Yes Sire, the very same,"
said Silas.

"Let me see it.
Where is this creature?
How much do you want?
I can see it feature
as a main attraction
(take it from me!).
The centre piece of the menagerie!"

"Well steady on now, please slow down,
I must first inform you of some facts.
You see there are some special dietary needs
on account of an unusual digestive tract.
Also, Sire, you must take care,
for it can be a little vicious.
See, the problem is, the gryphon, well,
you could call it perhaps....capricious.
One of the reasons may well be
that it only mates for life, you see.
And when the other party dies,
it's had enough. It never tries
to find another mate.
But also, we must discuss remuneration.
You must appreciate my business needs.
There's the matter of compensation.
After all, she provides me with 'gryphon's eggs',
which are very much sought after.
If I sell my prize asset, well,
I'll be poorer now hereafter."

"But I thought you said it had no mate?"
remonstrated a perplexed Gawain.
"So how can it lay eggs for you to sell?
Come on man, explain!"

"Well, Sire, it's like a laying hen.
It produces eggs, whenever.
But the eggs are only a side-line.
For the crux of this endeavour
is the biggest earner of the lot.

The gryphon's feathers are a cure
for them people what has got blindness.
It's a fact Sire, that's for sure!
It's documented and what's more,
I've helped a few afflicted souls
just out of human kindness.
But normally, I sell an occasional feather,
but you can't take too many at once.
See, obviously they have to grow back,
or else we'd have a gryphon with a bald bird's bonce!
And that would be no use to man or beast
For the gryphon, well, she's very proud.
Her self-esteem would be affected
and she'd probably need a shroud.
This would defeat the other opportunities
for economic wealth creation,
which is modelling for heraldry
and the statues outside stations.

So, in line with my long-term business plan
(well, you can see, you're an intelligent man!)
I'll have to cover my future lost earnings,
plus corporation tax and the cost of learning
a new trade or buying new livestock.
I'd never get another gryphon.
Although I do have a mate who developed an act
which he perfoms involving a python."

Sir Gawain said, "Now, honest yeoman,
I need time to consider this matter.
There are questions I feel that I need to explore,
away from your polished sales-patter."

"In that case Sire, I'll go to the bar
and get you a pint and a platter.
You can consider in perfect peace.
I'll tell the blokes in the Snug not to natter."

And Silas retired to the adjoining room,
then went for a walk outside,
where he danced a slip-jig with a saddle-back pig
and laughed till he almost cried.

Sir Gawain spent some time in deep thought :
'This seems like a perfect opportunity.
One that's much too good to ignore.
It's fantastic, it must be my lucky day.
An exotic creature, and what's more
it just dropped into my lap!
I don't have to fight any dragons,
or get sea-sick on the deck of a ship,
or black and blue travelling in wagons.

A gryphon! The mythical 'mystical' gryphon!
Wait till the sceptics at Camelot see it.
The looks on their faces, the gasps they'll emit.
I'll be feted, top rated and then celebrated.
Commended, applauded and congratulated,
Magnified, glorified. Oh my Lord, if I'd
only one wish in my life that I'd buy.....

"Landlord, Landlord, bring me Silas in here.
I'm pinching myself to ensure this is real.
For I'm about to construct and conduct
a life- changing business deal."

Silas returned from the backyard.
"You alright? Have you been shedding a tear?"
asked the slightly groggy Sir Gawain.

"Sorry, Sire. It's just that I fear that
if I sell you my wonderful gryphon,
well, who knows what the future may bring?
She's become like one of the family.
It's like selling your own offspring."

"Listen Silas, my man, I've decided
to set you in luxury for the rest of your life.
You'll be most handsomely rewarded."

"Well, thank you, Sire. And my wife?"

"Yes, she will receive similar treatment.
I'll tend to the matter straightaway."

"Sire if you don't mind me being a bit forward,
can I have it in cash today?"

"Well, I don't know, that's most unusual.
You can appear a bit brusque."

"Well if you get the dosh, Sire, I'll go home for a wash
and I'll meet you back here at dusk.
I'll bring back with me Greta Gryphon
(that's the name that we call her at home).
It'll be hard to part with her. All the same,
I'll throw in her bedding and comb."

So, Gawain settled down with a tankard
and a couple of more helpings of pie.

Then he staggered to his room
to count out some gold
and to get a little shut-eye.

Dusk arrives and Sir Gawain is supping,
when there's a knock on the tavern door.
A voice calls out for the esteemed Knight
and he crosses the tap-room floor.

There in the gloom is Silas Camm
with a suitcase and a sack.
And tied to the wall in the darkness
is a creature, grey and black.

"Well, it grieves me much to come to this,
but there she is, Sire, in all her glory.
Her bedding and comb, I've put in this sack
with legal papers about her life-story.
Which is important Sire, though I say it myself,
because she **is** the genuine bees-knees.
and there's a lot of chancers and sharks about.
You can sleep in your bed with ease.

But please, Sire, treat her with great care.
You can do what you like through the day
But at night she must be left alone,
Don't disturb her, or she might fly away.
This would, of course, be a terrible disaster.
So tonight, just leave her be.
You can get to know her in the morning.
I do hope she gets over me."

"Well, thank you Silas. What can I say?
It's been a privilege to do business with you."
Gold coins were exchanged and counted,
A bill of sale changed hands too.

"Well, will you stop and celebrate
this transaction with an quart of ale?"

"Oh, I'm sorry Sire, I've got to dash
I've an appointment about buying a whale.
It's a new business venture you see
and I don't want to miss the sale.
The wife and me, are excited
about the opening new horizon,
so we decided on the leviathan.
It was the first thing that she set her eyes on.
So, fare thee well, adieu and most of all good bye."
And with that, Silas Camm was gone
In the blinking of an eye.

Sir Gawain carefully checked the rope
that tied the gryphon to the wall.
Then he returned to the tap room
And he bellowed a hearty call.

"Landlord, fill my goblet up
with your finest, strongest ale.
I've cause for celebration,
based on this here bill of sale.

I've done a deal with Silas Camm.
Strange to say, he never tarried.
He had to rush off with his wife."
And the landlord said,
"Yes, Sire, that's very strange.
Silas isn't married."

And Sir Gawain looked at the bill of sale
And on that paper were the words:

1 Gryphon (sold as seen)
1 Gryphon bed
1 Gryphon comb

All hopefully sold to a loving home.

Sold this day by

Silas Camm

Signature:
S. Camm

He carefully folded up the docket
and placed it in his breast pocket.
"This is my ticket to fortune and fame.
"My word, I am a lucky man."
said Sir Gawain.

About the Author

Over the years Dave has worked in a range of creative fields: performing and writing music, sculpting and as a trainer writing and delivering scenarios and problem-solving activities for delivering stimulating activities and events.

'My musical output has almost always concentrated on instrumental compositions. Whatever the inspirations; jazz, classical, blues etc, the work is organic.

I LOVE IMPROVISATION AND TO EXPERIMENT.

My drawing and sculpting tends to be spontaneous. I do not start from a written, concrete concept or idea. I see something suggesting itself to me and then see where it takes me.

I have always enjoyed words.
I love the nuances and subtleties.
I adore idiom and accent.'

Although Dave has written many poems and short stories over the years his first published title was A Fishy Tail in 2010 in hardback with CD and also as a standalone AudioBook.

Dave currently lives and works in North Wales where he writes, records and runs his slate art workshop (Parc Glynllifon, Gwynnedd). Somehow Dave also finds time to sail his boat, climb, walk and paint!

Anyone wishing to book Dave for an event please contact him via his website www.davestephen.com